Gary Bower
2010

a Bright Future Book

The Jingle in my Pocket

Sound Money Principles That Kids Can Bank On

by Gary Bower
Illustrated by Jan Bower

STORYBOOK MEADOW PUBLISHING COMPANY
Traverse City, Michigan
www.STORYBOOKMEADOW.com

For our twelve children and their children,
to help keep their pockets jingling and their future bright.

The Jingle In My Pocket

Text Copyright © 2009 by Gary D. Bower
Illustrations Copyright © 2009 by Jan Bower
Published by Storybook Meadow Publishing Company
7700 Timbers Trail, Traverse City, MI 49684

ISBN: 978-0-9704621-9-0
Cover and interior design by Gary Bower
Printed and bound in Canada

There's a jingle in my pocket as I hum a happy tune.
I just earned a dollar and it isn't even noon!
When I reach into my pocket, it gives me such a tickle
to know I have two shiny dimes, three quarters and a nickel.

"...he who gathers money
little by little makes it grow."
~ Proverbs 13:11 (NIV)

"Whoever can be trusted with very little
can also be trusted with much..."
~ Luke 16:10 (NIV)

3

I earned the money honestly by working very hard. I helped a neighbor lady do some chores around her yard.

"Work hard and cheerfully at whatever you do, as though you were working for the Lord rather than for people."
~ Colossians 3:23 (NLT)

"Take a lesson from the ants, you lazybones. Learn from their ways and be wise! Even though they have no prince, governor, or ruler to make them work, they labor hard all summer, gathering food for the winter."
~ Proverbs 6:6-8 (NLT)

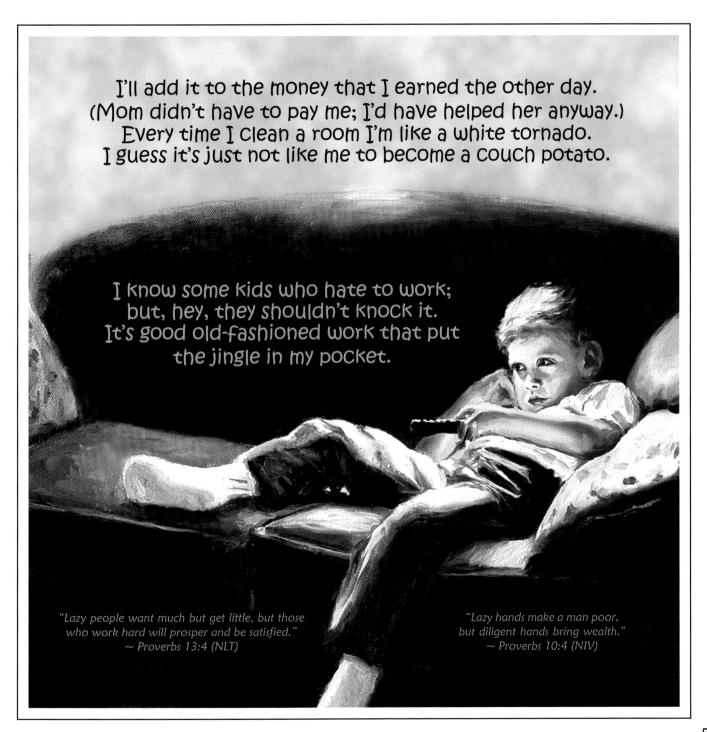

I'll add it to the money that I earned the other day.
(Mom didn't have to pay me; I'd have helped her anyway.)
Every time I clean a room I'm like a white tornado.
I guess it's just not like me to become a couch potato.

I know some kids who hate to work;
but, hey, they shouldn't knock it.
It's good old-fashioned work that put
the jingle in my pocket.

*"Lazy people want much but get little, but those
who work hard will prosper and be satisfied."*
~ Proverbs 13:4 (NLT)

*"Lazy hands make a man poor,
but diligent hands bring wealth."*
~ Proverbs 10:4 (NIV)

My mind begins to daydream
of the things that I could buy,
like candy, gum, or sundaes
with the ice cream piled high.
I think I'll spend my money
when my cousin comes to visit.
I'll have a ball, 'cuz after all,
the money's mine – or is it?

*"The silver is mine, and the gold
is mine, says the Lord Almighty."
~ Haggai 2:8 (NLT)*

*"...a foolish man devours all he has."
~ Proverbs 21:20 (NIV)*

*"...though your riches increase,
do not set your heart on them."
~ Psalms 62:10 (NIV)*

*"Those who love pleasure will become poor..."
~ Proverbs 21:17 (NLT)*

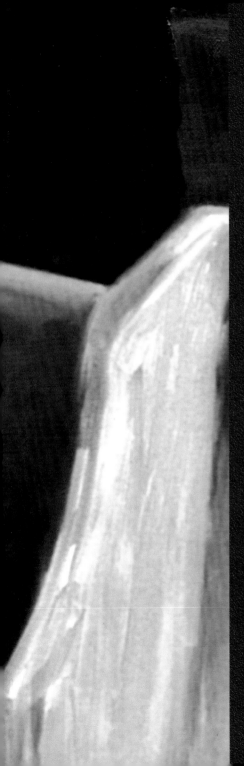

It's God who gives the skill to work,
the strength, the breath, the time.
The least that I can give to Him
is ten percent – a dime.
For everything I have today
has come at God's expense.
So gladly now I'm humming
to the tune of ninety cents.

$1.00
-.10
.90

"Lord...all we have accomplished is really from you."
~ Isaiah 26:12 (NLT)

*"But remember the Lord your God, for it is he who gives
you the ability to produce wealth..."*
~ Deuteronomy 8:18 (NIV)

*"Honor the Lord with your wealth, with the firstfruits of all your crops;
then your barns will be filled to overflowing..."*
~ Proverbs 3:9-10 (NIV)

"Bring the whole tithe into the storehouse..."
~ Malachi 3:10 (NIV)

*"Store your treasures in heaven...Wherever your treasure is,
there your heart and thoughts will also be."*
~ Matthew 6:20-21 (NLT)

*"Each man should give what he has decided in his heart to give,
not reluctantly or under compulsion, for God loves a cheerful giver."*
~ 2 Corinthians 9:7 (NIV)

Often, things will catch my eye in stores or magazines.
Constantly they're tempting me to live beyond my means.
A voice inside me says, "You need this thing, no doubt about it.
If you don't buy it now, you'll be the only kid without it!"
It's almost irresistible; I want it now, not later.
But wisdom calls and urges me to be a patient waiter.
I just might find it even cheaper at another store,
or maybe I'll find something else that I like even more.
I'll think about it for a day or two, for I am trying
to make decisions carefully and stop the "impulse-buying."

"...I have learned how to get along happily whether I have much or little."
~ Philippians 4:11 (NLT)

"Tell those who are rich in this world...not to trust in their money, which will soon be gone.
But their trust should be in the living God, who richly gives us all we need for our enjoyment."
~ I Timothy 6:17 (NLT)

"Watch out! Be on your guard against all kinds of greed; a man's life does not consist in the abundance of his possessions."
~ Luke 12:15 (NIV)

Money wants to fly away.
It takes off like a rocket.
If I'm not careful it can burn
a hole right through my pocket.
Many things that tempt the eyes
may give a short-lived tingle,
but later I'll discover that
they've robbed me of my jingle.
There's a time for spending, sure,
and there's a time for saving.
The time to spend is when I'm thinking,
not when I am craving.

"For riches can disappear as though they had the wings of a bird!"
~ Proverbs 23:5 (NLT)

"Those who love money will never have enough. How absurd to think that wealth brings true happiness!"
~ Ecclesiastes 5:10 (NLT)

"For the love of money is at the root of all kinds of evil."
~ 1 Timothy 6:10 (NLT)

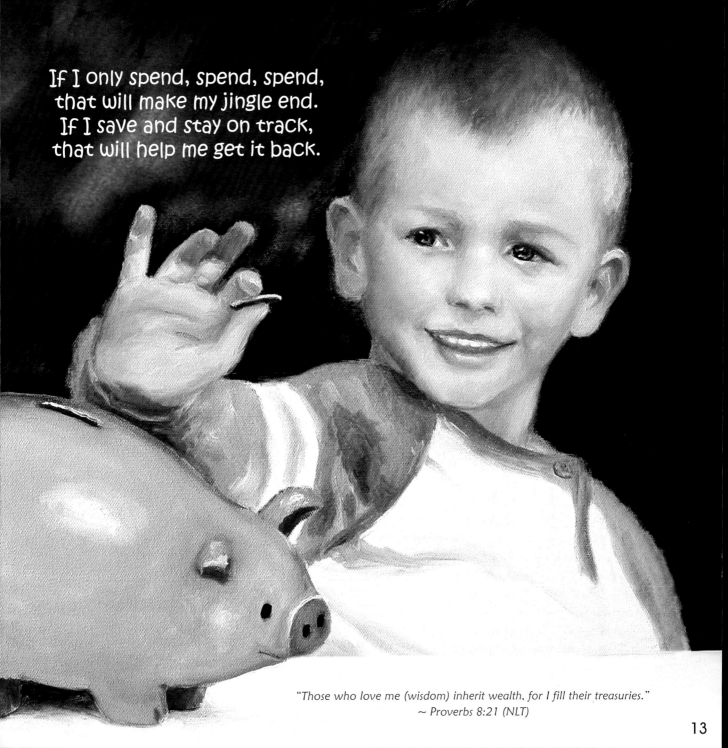

If I only spend, spend, spend,
that will make my jingle end.
If I save and stay on track,
that will help me get it back.

"Those who love me (wisdom) inherit wealth, for I fill their treasuries."
~ Proverbs 8:21 (NLT)

13

Earning money's really fun!
I'd like to earn some more.
I look around to see if I
can find another chore.
I'm sure I have a lot of skills
that someone, somewhere needs.
I wonder...could I wash Dad's car
or help Mom pull the weeds?

Hmmm...

I know! Grandma's flowers!
I'll make sure they're watered well...

"I walked by the field of a lazy person...I saw that it was overgrown with thorns. It was covered with weeds, and its walls were broken down. Then, as I looked and thought about it, I learned this lesson: A little extra sleep, a little more slumber, a little folding of the hands to rest – and poverty will pounce on you like a bandit; scarcity will attack you like an armed robber."
~ Proverbs 24:30-34 (NLT)

"All hard work brings a profit, but mere talk leads only to poverty."
~ Proverbs 14:23 (NIV)

"Wealth from get-rich-quick schemes quickly disappears; wealth from hard work grows."
~ Proverbs 13:11 (NLT)

"Do you see any truly competent workers? They will serve kings rather than ordinary people."
~ Proverbs 22:29 (NLT)

...and I might walk the neighbor's dog,
or bake some things to sell.

"Good planning and hard work lead to prosperity, but hasty shortcuts lead to poverty."
~ Proverbs 21:5 (NLT)

"The laborer's appetite works for him; his hunger drives him on."
~ Proverbs 16:26 (NIV)

I just had a great idea! There's money to be made
by setting up a stand outside and selling lemonade.
I look inside the cupboard. Now here's some happy news!
I see a five-pound bag of sugar Mom might let me use.
Mom says, "Not a problem. It all sounds really great.
Now that will be...oh, let me see...a dollar-ninety-eight."
I reach into my pocket. Hmm...things are looking bad.
Maybe I can borrow it. I'll go and talk to Dad.
I need a bag of lemons, too. Why wait before I get it?
People do it all the time; they're "buying things on credit."
I can pay Dad later when my bank is overflowing.
It shouldn't take much time at all to get my business going.

But...

...what if all my big ideas don't turn out that way?
I'd get stuck with lemons and a debt I can't repay.
I guess it really wouldn't hurt to save a little longer.
Without a doubt, without a debt
my business will be stronger.

So...

...I walk the neighbor's dog again; then I pull some weeds,
and soon my piggy bank has all the capital it needs.

"Now listen, you who say, 'Today or tomorrow we will...carry on business and make money.'
Why, you do not even know what will happen tomorrow."
~ James 4:13-14 (NIV)

"...the borrower is servant to the lender."
~ Proverbs 22:7 (NIV)

Now I'm free to concentrate on making lemonade.
It sure feels mighty good to know
that all my bills are paid.

"Let no debt remain outstanding,
except the continuing debt to love one another..."
~ Romans 13:8 (NIV)

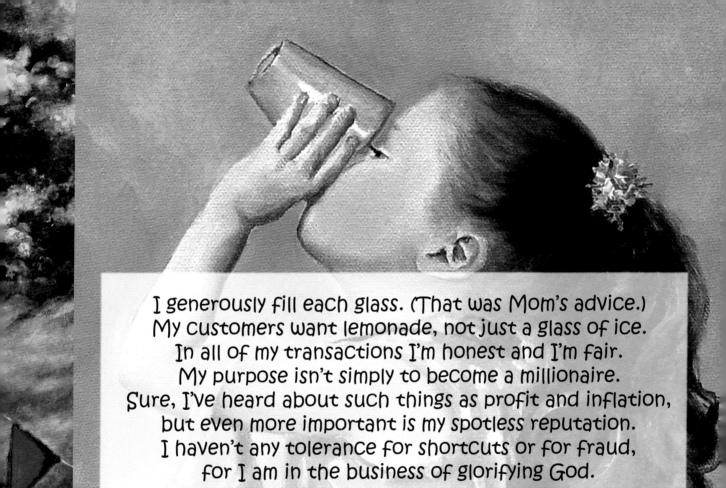

I generously fill each glass. (That was Mom's advice.)
My customers want lemonade, not just a glass of ice.
In all of my transactions I'm honest and I'm fair.
My purpose isn't simply to become a millionaire.
Sure, I've heard about such things as profit and inflation,
but even more important is my spotless reputation.
I haven't any tolerance for shortcuts or for fraud,
for I am in the business of glorifying God.

Look at all the lemonade my neighbors are consuming!
My customers are happy and my sales are really booming.
When a person's satisfied with something he has found,
he tells a friend and very quickly word just gets around.

*"All goes well for those who are generous, who
lend freely and conduct their business fairly."*
~ Psalms 112:5 (NLT)

*"A good name is more desirable than great riches;
to be esteemed is better than silver or gold."*
~ Proverbs 22:1 (NIV)

I think I'd like to plant some seeds.
I'll water and I'll hoe.
I hope the things that I invest
eventually will grow.

I made a hefty profit.
So, now what should I do?
My pocket's really heavy.
Dad says, "It's up to you."
First of all,
some goes to God
for I have Him to thank.
Next, I put a healthy sum
inside my piggy bank.
After that, my Mom and I
decide we'd like to shop.
We're in the garden section
when, suddenly, I stop.

"He who works his land will have abundant food..."
~ Proverbs 12:11 (NIV)

"...a farmer who plants only a few seeds will
get a small crop. But the one who plants
generously will get a generous crop."
~ 2 Corinthians 9:6 (NLT)

Though I'm not always patient,
I am happy in the end
when I see my small investment
pay a juicy dividend.

I'll handle money God's way,
for He's a great rewarder.
Giving, saving, spending –
that's the proper order.
And if it ever comes about
that I am extra-blessed,
I'll take that little surplus
and carefully invest.
For when I discipline myself
with habits that are wise,
my money doesn't disappear.
Instead, it multiplies!

"...the root of the righteous flourishes."
~ Proverbs 12:12 (NIV)

"A sluggard does not plow in season;
so at harvest time he looks but finds nothing."
~ Proverbs 20:4 (NIV)

I know that life is not about
accumulating stuff.
And while it's true that I've been blessed,
for some, these times are tough.
So help me see the hurting, Lord.
Don't let my heart be greedy.
Instead, I want to live my faith
by caring for the needy.
For when I share my blessings
with a neighbor who's in trouble,
a happy miracle occurs;
I see Your blessings double.

"Give freely without begrudging it, and the Lord your God
will bless you in everything you do."
~ Deuteronomy 15:10 (NLT)

"He who is kind to the poor lends to the Lord, and
he will reward him for what he has done."
~ Proverbs 19:17 (NIV)

"A generous man will himself be blessed, for he shares his food with the poor."
~ Proverbs 22:9 (NIV)

"Feed the hungry and help those in trouble. Then your light will shine out
from the darkness, and the darkness around you will be as bright as day."
~ Isaiah 58:10 (NLT)

"Give, and it will be given to you. A good measure, pressed down,
shaken together and running over, will be poured into your lap."
~ Luke 6:38 (NIV)

"It is more blessed to give than to receive."
~ Acts 20:35 (NIV)

There's a jingle in my pocket as I hum a happy tune.
Oh, I might never grow to be a well-to-do tycoon.
I might not drive a fancy car. I might not own a yacht,
or wear designer clothes; in fact, I might not own a lot.
But if I'm wise and diligent, I know that I'll succeed.
By following God's principles I'll have the things I need;
not just enough to get me by, but also some to spare.
It's nice to have a little extra "jingle" just to share.
Riches do not grip me. My heart is money-free,
for I don't serve my money. No, my money works for me.
I only have one Master; not gold, not cash, not jewels.
I serve the One who made it all, and over all He rules.
Me? I'm just a steward, and this life's a testing ground.
Instead of craving riches, I long to hear one sound.
By learning to be faithful with all that I possess...

"Look at the birds of the air...your heavenly Father feeds them. Are you not much more valuable than they?
...See how the lilies of the field grow...not even Solomon in all his splendor was dressed like one of these.
If that is how God clothes the grass of the field...will he not much more clothe you, O you of little faith?
So do not worry...your heavenly Father knows that you need them. But seek first his kingdom
and his righteousness, and all these things will be given to you as well."
~ Matthew 6:26-33 (NIV)

...someday I'll hear the words,
"Well done!"
Now <u>that</u> is true success!

"No one can serve two masters. Either he will hate the one and love the other, or he will
be devoted to the one and despise the other. You cannot serve both God and money."
~ Matthew 6:24 (NIV)

"His master replied, 'Well done, good and faithful servant! You have been faithful with a few things;
I will put you in charge of many things. Come and share your master's happiness!'"
~ Matthew 25:21, 23 (NIV)

A Wealth of Wisdom

Famous Quotes
to help keep your
pocket jingling &
your heart humming

"The dictionary is the only place where success comes before work."

– Vince Lombardi, *Hall of Fame NFL coach*

"Opportunity is missed by most because it is dressed in overalls and looks like work."

– Thomas A. Edison, *American Inventor*

"Begin with determination to succeed, and the work is half done already."

– Mark Twain, *American author and humorist*

"When you play, play hard; when you work, don't play at all."

– Theodore Roosevelt, *26th President of the United States*

"The safest way to double your money is to fold it over and put it in your pocket."

– Kin Hubbard, *American cartoonist and humorist*

"You can't have a perfect day without doing something for someone who'll never be able to repay you."

– John Wooden, *Hall of Fame NCAA basketball coach*

"The value of a man resides in what he gives and not in what he is capable of receiving."

– Albert Einstein, *American scientist*

"We make a living by what we get, but we make a life by what we give."

– Sir Winston Churchill, *British Prime Minister*

"If you can't feed a hundred people, then feed just one."

– Mother Teresa, *Albanian missionary to India*

"No legacy is so rich as honesty."

– William Shakespeare, *English poet and playwright*

"If a person gets his attitude toward money straight, it will help straighten out almost every other area in his life."

– Dr. Billy Graham, *American evangelist*

"The only things we can keep are the things we freely give to God."

– C.S. Lewis, *British Author*

"In God We Trust"

These words first appeared on a U.S. coin in 1864. Since 1938 all U.S. coins bear this inscription. *In God We Trust* became the official national motto of the U.S.A. by an Act of Congress in 1956. Here are things said by some of the people we honor on our currency and coins:

George Washington
1st President of the United States

"Worry is the interest paid by those who borrow trouble."

"Associate with men of good quality if you esteem your own reputation; for it is better to be alone than in bad company."

"Let your heart feel for the afflictions and distress of everyone, and let your hand give in proportion to your purse."

Abraham Lincoln
16th President of the United States

"That some achieve great success is proof to all that others can achieve it as well."

"Let not him who is houseless pull down the house of another, but let him work diligently and build one for himself."

"Give me six hours to chop down a tree, and I will spend the first hour sharpening my axe."

Thomas Jefferson
3rd President of the United States

"Never spend your money before you have it."

"I find that the harder I work, the more luck I seem to have."

"Determine never to be idle."

Franklin D. Roosevelt
32nd President of the United States

"It isn't sufficient just to want; you've got to ask yourself what you are going to do to get the things you want."

John F. Kennedy
35th President of the United States

"[A man] once asked his gardener to plant a tree. When the gardener objected that the tree was slow growing and would not reach maturity for 100 years, [the man] replied, 'In that case, there is no time to lose; plant it this afternoon.'"

Alexander Hamilton
1st Treasury Secretary of the United States

"Men give me credit for genius. All the genius I have lies in this: When I have a subject in hand, I study it profoundly. ...People are pleased to call [this effort] the fruit of genius. It is the fruit of labor and thought."

"Those who stand for nothing fall for anything."

Andrew Jackson
7th President of the United States

"You must pay the price if you wish to secure the blessing."

"Any man worth his salt will stick up for what he believes is right; but it takes a slightly better man to acknowledge... without reservation that he is in error."

Ulysses S. Grant
18th President of the United States

"Hold fast to the Bible. To the influence of this Book we are indebted for all the progress made in true civilization, and to this we must look as our guide in the future."

"In every battle there comes a time when both sides consider themselves beaten. He who continues the attack wins."

Benjamin Franklin
American statesman, inventor and author

"A penny saved is a penny earned."

"Beware of small expenses; a small leak will sink a great ship."

"Early to bed and early to rise makes a man healthy, wealthy and wise."

"Contentment makes poor men rich; discontentment makes rich men poor."

How To Keep Your Pocket Jingling

*"And my God will meet all your needs according
to his glorious riches in Christ Jesus."*
~ Philippians 4:19 (NIV)

Here are things that kids should know:
Good times come and good times go.
Don't buy everything you crave.
You will prosper if you save.
Have a plan for what to spend.
View your budget as a friend.
Only see the ice cream man
if your budget says you can.
Things of worth are worth the wait.
Work, then you can celebrate.
Those who try to get-rich-quick
get the short end of the stick.
Don't believe what can't be true.
Don't let greed bamboozle you.
Stay away from schemes and bets.
Always, always pay your debts.
When you find you're up a tree,
take responsibility.
Don't repeat the same mistakes.
Minimize your coffee breaks.
Every day, in every quest,
always try to do your best.
Further blessing you'll ensure
if you choose to help the poor.
Things taste sweeter when you share.
Never covet or compare.

Strive for fairness. Never cheat.
No one lives on Easy Street.
Don't buy what you can't afford.
Don't be stingy with the Lord.
Try to finish what you start.
Don't let money seize your heart.
Know that money's just a tool.
He who loves it is a fool.
Cherish people and invest
in Heaven's priceless treasure chest.
Worldly wealth is fading fast.
God's eternal Word will last.
Though the things of earth may dim,
you can always bank on Him.

~ Gary Bower

About the Author & Illustrator

Gary and Jan Bower are rich with twelve kids and an ever-growing portfolio of grandchildren. They enjoy investing their time and talents in the lives of young families by writing and illustrating books that can help parents guide their children to a brighter future. **The Jingle in My Pocket** is their tenth book together, and third in their **"Bright Future"** series. The Bowers live in Traverse City, Michigan. You may order their books and art prints, and learn more about their family and ministry, by visiting them at **www.bowerbooks.com**.